Standing
Tall

This book is published by
Standing Tall Press

ISBN 978-1-0687665-5-8

Standing Tall

Living with Motor Neurone Disease

Samantha Whittaker

with contributions from
Adam Levene

Standing Tall Press

Standing Tall

Samantha Whittaker was born in Windsor, Berkshire. She has a BA (Hons) in English and Philosophy from Kent University at Canterbury and a Master's in Community Psychology (with Distinction) from Brighton University. After graduating from Kent, Sam entered book publishing as a marketing assistant for a major international publisher. She worked in publishing for several different companies over a 20-year period and rose to the position of editorial director for a leading publishing house. Sam then worked for the CIPD (Chartered Institute of Personnel Development) before retraining as a facilitator working for several social enterprises. She has also been a Visiting Lecturer at Oxford Brookes University on their publishing courses. Sam has had a lifelong love of poetry and literature and this is her first book. She lives in Brighton with her husband and two daughters.

Acknowledgements

I would like to thank Steve Hardman, my husband, for being so committed to publishing this poetry and art therapy book. His dedication, perseverance and full-on tenacity meant that my book came into Being.

I would also like to thank Adam Levene for being such an outstanding art therapist and just a compassionate human being. He worked tirelessly on this poetry and art therapy book: making the book cover, images, even typesetting the poems. We go as a family to these sessions with Adam and we have such rich and meaningful conversations, I would wholeheartedly recommend him.

Adam introduced us to Michèle Wood, Vice-chair of the British Association of Art Therapists, at an exhibition at Sussex University and we had a very warm and interesting conversation with her. I would like to thank her for her generosity in writing the foreword and her support for this book.

Jeff Scott, with his insight and flair, did the publicity for the book and Natalie Wills, with her creativity and energy, provided her marketing expertise. I would also like to thank Graham Russel for copyediting the manuscript.

I dedicate this book to my dad,
William Bowker Whittaker –
he was taken too early from us.

Contents

Part 2: Art therapy

Foreword

I was privileged to meet Sam and Steve at the exhibition *What does living with Motor Neurone Disease look like? Art Therapy in practice* in July 2024. Our conversation took in the enormity of what it means to be living with MND, while setting that in the wider context of the power of creativity. The exhibition of art therapy pictures and poems that surrounded us as we spoke gave voice to this. I had just finished watching the video presentations that accompanied the exhibition, in which Steve, Sam and their daughters feature, and was feeling deeply moved by their love and eloquence.

I was also impressed by the support given by the West Sussex South and East Sussex Motor Neurone Disease Association (MNDA) regional branches for my friend and colleague Adam Levene's sensitive therapeutic work. Listening to Steve and Sam explain how valuable their art therapy sessions with Adam have been, I could not have been prouder of my profession or more convinced of how significant a role art therapy can play in the care of people living with MND.

The psychotherapeutic relationship of art therapy is private and personal, and safely held within the bounds of confidentiality. As such, the depth of meaning within the artworks can easily be missed by a casual viewer. Sam and Steve's generous decision to share insights into their family's personal experiences of MND will go a long way to demonstrating the value and impact of art therapy. Readers of this beautiful volume will gain an understanding of the importance of conversations made possible through imagery, analogy and metaphor. They will learn of the value of art therapy to make space to reflect, to share emotions and to connect with others. Yet *Standing Tall* is not only about art therapy, but about Sam's poetic vision of the world, about life's big questions, and most of all about love. This is a wonderful book that is "Joyfully Serious".

Michèle JM Wood
HCPC Art Psychotherapist
BA(Hons), PGDIp, MA, MRes, CF, CSAccred (CP)
Vice-chair British Association of Art Therapists

Part 1:
Poems

Introduction by Samantha Whittaker

I have always been a lover of poetry – I remember I even wrote a poem for my husband, Steve, and read it out during the speeches at our wedding lunch. I started 'Voices' whilst at University with a group of friends – it was a creative new magazine for poetry, prose and artwork.

I wrote poems in my 20s, but then life took over. I entered a career in publishing – academic, professional and textbooks. I then had two daughters – at age 33 I had Evie and at 35 I had Elise. I am so proud of them – they are wondrous, amazing, and fabulous! My husband, Steve, has Grace peeking over one shoulder and Kindness the other – you couldn't hope for a more gracious man.

On June 8th 2023, I was told I had bulbar MND – it's a condition where you start with slurred speech. I started writing poetry when I got my diagnosis. I don't want MND to define me.

People would often describe me as Joyfully Serious – I was serious about the world and the people in it but also quite joyful at times. I remember our plane was delayed in Sardinia and we were sitting in a disco café – I remember dancing to the tunes with wild abandon. I was sitting on a train and this man was shouting at his partner – she had two small children with her. I went and stood between the man and his partner – I asked her if she was okay. I went to Pride (I live in Brighton) and this Drag Queen was asking for people to dance in a Dance Off – I volunteered myself – I even have it on my daughter's video on her iPhone. I remember talking on Radio Sussex about period poverty.

I have always been fascinated in metaphysical issues – why do we exist in the world? I have these conversations with Brendan – or Bren for short. Someone that I hold dear to me is Sarah – I just love hanging out with her. When my speech went, I would write down what I felt about the world – political conversations!

I would like to reach out to my family and friends – the generosity and kindness you have shown me cannot be put into words. I love you all.

A Summer Memory

Memory sums up being a long time in the past,
A long time ago – where smells, textures, photographs
    evoke something.
This memory was very recent – July in fact.
We went out into the East Sussex countryside,
Where the paragliders hang like mobiles in the sky
And the Downs gently pull you into their embrace.

We walked.
With skylarks singing high above our heads,
And then silence – like a Quaker meeting –
– Before they plunged into the ochre and green fields.
And swallows divebombing amongst the subdued
    yellow wheat,
And corn buntings perching in the hedgerows.
A harmonious orchestra of sounds and vibrations
Punctuated by the plaintive bleating from black-faced sheep.

We climbed.
Exuberant clouds scudding high above our heads,
Fat and fluffy,
With light bobbing around the fields,
A dancing chimera of shade and light
The light always breaking through the darkness.

We descended.

Always with Berwick Church spire in our sights.

Butterflies lined our path as we descended,

Bright, colourful, pirouetting and plie-ing.

An assembly of red admirals, chequered white, and
    painted ladies,

A carpet of colours to pave our way.

Entering St Michael's and All Angels Church that day,

I marvelled at the murals painted with such loving care.

The Italian-style frescos painted on the pulpit,

The circular seasons painted on the Sanctuary,

The Annunciation, the Crucifixion and Jesus in Their Glory.

This moved me – awe and grace toppled over each other.

All the Angels were there that day.

Seashells

Lift it to your ear
Where oh where is it from?
High on a rock,
Or deep in the ocean.
In a rock pool
Lying on a beach.

The common cockle,
Fan shaped with ridges and grooves.
A mussel or common oysters.
The spired whelk or the colourful periwinkle,
You can find all these adornments,
Closer to home than you think.

Necklace shell – patterned into intricate meanings,
Slipper limpet to cushion your feet – or not!
Tools, currency, spiritual objects,
Ornaments,
The seashell has always fascinated us humans.

A home to many a mollusc,
That's where they started life.
Outer skeletons that save the beast within,
Calcium carbonate to protect the creature inside,
Shades of mottled brown or coal black,
Or delicate pink or sandy yellow.

A pearl shining brightly on the beach,
Or a razor clam that looks like it will be at home
    in the barber shop,
Grey or white limpets that hang off every rock,
Clams that live just below the sand or mud,
Or painted topshells housing snails.

When you walk on the beach,
Or go rock pooling,
Remember, remember the little creatures,
That inhabit the sand, or the mud or the deep,
These are special creatures,
Mind how you go when beach combing.

Brighton Skies

Did you see the magnificent sky?
An ochre red to match the ladybird.
Or even a ruby red reminiscent of the toadstool.
Cluttering clouds reminding me of windswept whisps,
A jumbling, tumbling tumult of billowing smoke.
Cast your eye up to see the painterly, creative sky.

Swifts paraglide, feasting on insects,
Do you see how sociable they are?
Wheeling over roof-tops, calling to each other,
Often in groups.
Do you see their forked tail?
And how their wings arch.

Herring gulls catcall to each other,
Do you hear them squawking?
Done up in their sailor's suit,
Fighting over a chip.
Do you see their pink legs?
And how the sun catches their white wings?

How much do we really see the world?
The roses, or the lilac blooms,
The tree standing steadfast,
Upright and honest and genuine,
Or the squirrel feasting on the nuts,
Or the blackbird singing in the tree.

How much do we really see?

Hello

To me 'hello' is a precious word,
People use it day-to-day,
To me 'hello' is a magical word,
To me 'hello' is a sublime word.

People shorten it to 'hi',
But I have no truck with that.
Or Dear, but that seems too formal.
Hello - does it for me.

I feel safe when I say 'hello',
I feel safe when they say 'hello' back,
I feel safe. Full stop.
Safe to be me.

Love

Love,
You can't hold it,
It's not a physicality to devour,
(Or maybe it is?)

It has a multitude of meanings,
Eros – romantic love,
Storge – familial love,
Philia – platonic love,
Love is a moveable feast,
It's slippery.

Why can one word hold so much meaning?
To treasure, to value, to respect, to cherish,
Compassionate commitment or passionate intent.
Conviction to a value,
Intimacy or affinity or narcissism.

Adoration, tenderness or just plain duty.
Longing, Obsession, Vulnerability, Enchanting.
Empathy, Vivaciousness, Openhearted, Loyal.

Love,

Is an elixir of kindness, passion, gentleness,

Affection, adoration, desire, devotion.

Love,

Is a halo that envelopes you,

And makes you feel safe.

Love,

Is a magical blessing of emotional appreciation,

And I have known it all.

Love.

Courage

What does courage mean?
Does it mean fighting, going into battle,
    being prepared?
The Dictionary defines it as,
"The ability to control your fear in a dangerous
    or difficult situation".
"Readiness to face or endure danger or difficulty".
Control, readiness…
    words that define being strong, robust, unfearful.

To me, courage is the courage to do the right thing,
Even if others around you are not.
Courage to face the fear and do it anyway.
Courage is showing gratitude and kindness.
Courage is slowing down and really
    understanding what is happening to someone else.
Courage is really listening and playing back for meaning.
    How often do we listen and really hear,
    (And how often do we listen to reply.)
Courage is practising patience, being kind and empathic.

Courage is facing into the meaninglessness
    of your current situation,
Facing into meaninglessness is a meaningful act.

Courage is the courage to be human,
Courage is living in the ambiguity – nothing is certain.

Courage is the 'courage to be'.

Empathy

To walk in the other person's shoes,
To take a different perspective from that which
    you hold dear.
To understand and be reasonable.
To consider their point of view,
But still believe in your own.

Emotional intelligence,
Emotional – the ability to tap into your own emotions,
And ponder.
Intelligence – self-awareness, learning,
We all make mistakes.

Sympathy,
Is feeling sad for the person,
But not relating.
Pity – feeling for someone,
But not grieving.

Empathy,
Feeling with someone,
Bear witness to their horror.
What that person is experiencing,
And all of their emotional turmoil.

Empathy – we could do with more.

Kindness

Empathy, tenderness, service,
Grace, benevolence, gentleness,
What is kindness to you?
Empathy is feeling WITH someone,
Slowing down to really hear what they are saying.

Tenderness is being gentle, loving,
Service is a blessing that you can bestow,
Grace is a powerful emotion,
Benevolence is a gift given out of generosity,
Gentleness is a present to be calm and responsive.

The famous quote
"It's better to give than receive"
Kindness is putting other peoples' needs first,
Small changes can make a big difference,
Platitudes that really mean something.

It can improve your wellbeing,
Mental health,
Kindly acts light up your brain,
Social anxiety lessens,
What is kindness?

Gratitude

Gratitude is not being 'nice',
Or nonchalant to people doing their best.
Gratitude is a feeling,
That pervades you.

Gratitude is being thankful for that moment,
Squeeze hold tight.
The most precious of moments to be savoured,
For life is ambiguous.

Gratitude is appreciating what life brings you,
Acknowledging all that you have,
For some don't have a home,
Or a bed or food.

Gratitude is recognising when times are tough for others,
And being kind to strangers,
A tribute to people who show you love,
Being responsive to their kindly attention.

Gratitude is not giving a damn,
But being appreciative of all that you hold dear.
A eulogy to those people who you want to thank,
Do it now.

Robust Vulnerability

Robust – powerful, strong, energetic,
Vulnerability – helplessness, defencelessness, unprotected,
What does it mean?

A person needs to balance these two qualities,
A person needs to sit in harmony with them,
How often do you feel affronted when everything
    isn't perfection?

Humans need to make mistakes to learn,
That is being vulnerable.
Being humble.

Humans need to show strength in the face of setbacks,
This is being robust,
Being tough.

Vulnerability is giving voice to others,
Robustness is courageously giving them the power to talk,
You learn.

How often do we think we have to know all the answers,
How often do we take one path,
And then double back.

How often do we laugh at ourselves,
In the presence of strangers,
Makes us vulnerable.

How often do we have the skill to be taught something,
As an adult,
That takes determination.

Robust – healthy, wholesome, well-conditioned,
Vulnerability – receptive, easiness, openness.
This is what it means.

Lost

In a maze you get lost
To find a magical centre.
You are proud at having navigated the twists and turns.
You are proud at not faltering.

In a labyrinth the path will lead you to the middle,
A long continuous road.
(Beware the Minotaur!)
You are proud at not faltering.

Sea mist laps at your Being,
Sea mist envelopes you.
Sea mist disappears,
You have found your Being again.

We all get lost to find ourselves.
Slowing down, gentle listening.
Empathy, integrity, gratitude, courage.
That is what is Being.

Lost is not feeling dislocation or overwhelm,
Lost is not losing yourself in a whirlpool of nothingness.
Lost is becoming stronger, seeking and finding,
Lost is knowing this person,
And the family that surrounds you.

This is what Being is.

One, Four, Three

It's a riddle – a conundrum,
An enigma or puzzle,
A mystery to be solved.
Is it a secret to be illuminated?
Or a problem to be unravelled?

A blue pen,
A pink dog,
A gold cat,
A jade bag,
A plum mum.

Hold up fingers (if you're signing),
Very simply put,

I LOVE YOU.

Joyfully Serious

Joyful – full of mischief and plenty of fun,
Serious – giving a damn about the world and
    the people in it.
Joyfully serious is a mixture of both!

Joyful – whipping out dance moves in airport lounges,
Playing 'internationale' to my daughters' friends,
Getting drunk, playing charades, not knowing when
    dinner will be ready.

Serious – talking about period poverty on the radio,
Putting myself between an angry man and his
    frightened wife,
And asking if she's okay.

Joyful – lively, eccentric,
Never knowing how I'll respond,
Unpredictable!

Serious – standing up to bigots (most of whom are men),
Commitment to the Trade Unions,
"Up the Workers!"

Pint drinking,
Disco dancing,
Tail wagging.

Meaning seeking,
Ambiguity navigating,
Curiously questioning.

Joyfully serious is an unpredictable thing,
It could be joyful, it could be serious.
But always predictably unpredictable!

P.S.

Not being understood,
Conclude, contemplate, construe,
Extrapolate, infer, speculate,
Rationalize, read, reason,
Words that sum up…

Saliva, saliva, saliva,
Secretions, slobber, spit,
Dribble, drool, drivel,
Phlegm, froth, mucus,
Words that sum up …

Hands that aren't functioning,
Operating, operational, operative,
Alive, active, action,
Working, workable, vitality,
Words that sum up…

Arms that are weakening,
Deterioration, decline, decay,
Exhaustion, enfeeblement, ebbing,
Sapping, setback, sinking,
Words that sum up…

Reason, slobber, alive, decline,
Words that sum up…

Where Will I Go?

Where will I go when the final curtain falls?
How will I get there?
How will I end?
All these uncertainties of living
…in the ambiguity.

Will I transcend to Heaven,
And meet my dad there?
Or perhaps I have multiple souls,
To be reborn as a spirit or an animal.
Or maybe none of the above.

Which faith do I align with?
Judaism is the 'parent' among the Abrahamic faiths.
Christianity centres on Jesus Christ,
Or Islam, or Hinduism, or Buddhism?
I know the Christian story well,
It's a good story.

Standing Tall

At 56 I was struck with this terrible disease,
MND – or Motor Neurone Disease.
Slurred speech – my GP knew something was wrong.
But I carry on – standing tall.

Nobody can understand me now,
I write things down, or use an App,
It's the mundane things I can't stand.
But I carry on – standing tall.

I feel isolated – I used to chat and laugh so much,
And eat – birthdays, celebrations, just life,
These things elude me.
But I carry on – standing tall.

My arms are weakening now,
As are my hands,
It's a challenge to dress myself (but I still manage it).
But I carry on – standing tall.

Standing tall – what does the dictionary say about that?
To support oneself on the feet in an erect position,
Or to maintain one's position – standing firm.
But I carry on – standing tall.

I would choose – to maintain one's position,
   standing firm,
It's a metaphor I aspire to,
(But I'm not very good at holding to it 100% of the time),
But I carry on – standing tall.

Standing tall is where you'll find me,
When I die.

Part 2:
Art therapy

Introduction by Adam Levene

Before introducing the practice of art therapy, let me begin with a few words about my art therapy experience.

I completed my Art Therapy Masters training in 2010. As an art therapist, I am state registered with the Health and Care Professions Council (HCPC). I am a BAAT (British Association of Art Therapists) registered Private Practitioner and practise from my garden studio in Lewes, East Sussex.

My work has been primarily supporting individuals, carers and families living or coping with the impact of life-limiting or life-threatening illness and injury.

Over the last 14 years I have facilitated individual and group art therapy sessions, for patients of the oncology department at St Bartholomew's Hospital, London, Marie Curie Hospice Hampstead and St Peter & St James Hospice in Chailey.

Since 2020 the West Sussex South branch of the MNDA, and, more recently the East Sussex branch, have been referring patients, carers and family members for art therapy.

What is art therapy?

Art therapy is a form of psychotherapy that uses visual and tactile media as a means of self expression and communication. Art therapists aim to support people of all ages and abilities and at all stages of life, to discover an outlet for often complex and confusing feelings, and foster self awareness and growth.

British Association of Art Therapists www.baat.org

This section of the book focuses on how art therapy has supported a very close and loving family, whose lives have been affected by MND, a life-limiting and life-threatening illness. However, art therapy also helps people of all ages, including those who often aren't as fortunate to have such support around them, whose lives have been affected by difficult personal or cultural experiences, illness and/or disability.

Over the next four pages, Sam, Steve, Evie and Elise talk openly about their personal art therapy experiences. The family's words are taken directly from a filmed interview presented at an exhibition hosted by the Brighton and Sussex Medical School and supported by the MNDA in July 2024, titled, *What does living with Motor Neurone Disease look like? Art Therapy in practice.*

Our family art therapy sessions together

When Sam heard about art therapy from the MNDA (despite being more into poetry and words), she really liked the concept, as did her family. Sam and I initially met over Zoom to talk about how the session might look. She seemed very excited to give it a try, especially when I invited her daughter, Evie, to accompany her. Sam attended the first session with Evie, then subsequently her husband Steve, and their other daughter, Elise, came along too. Having been initially offered funding by the MNDA for a block of six sessions, this was extended to a further twelve. At the point of going to print, we continue to have our incredibly moving art therapy sessions together.

Here, in their own words, is what they say about their art therapy experience and what it offered them, both individually and as a family.

Sam

If you have MND, you can use the left side of your brain for processing medical information in shorthand, but it's the right side of your brain for being creative and artistic. I write poetry, so it appealed to me to enter into unknown territory.

I didn't feel confident at art at school, but the art therapist, Adam, encourages you and I found comfort in being able to express myself using pastels, collage etc. It really opens up a new conversation with myself and my family around me.

It allowed us to open up and talk about things we never talk about. We naturally discuss things, and that is what is so powerful about art therapy.

I don't think speech restriction is an issue. I often bring Adam a poem, he reads it out. This contributes to some meaningful discussions. We then go on to do art. I write things down, and Adam always look first at me, so I don't feel excluded.

I always leave feeling brighter than when I joined. I have discovered so much with what is going on with my two daughters.

Evie

I was a little bit apprehensive about art therapy because I have no artistic ability whatsoever, but that doesn't matter.

I think it's a really good space for us to come together as a family. It doesn't feel like a really pressurised environment. We don't have to talk about things if we don't want to.

It's really good to have that space to talk about things and emotions and feelings that we wouldn't have spoken about.

Sometimes you can't necessarily find the words to express how you're feeling. Just through using photos and images and words I found in magazines, that say so much, Adam helps you unpack that and explore how you're feeling based on what you've cut out.

I always come away feeling a lot brighter, a lot lighter.

Elise

I can sometimes be a bit prone to push thing to the back of my head and not think about it, because obviously things are quite challenging. But sometimes Adam will have conversations before we start the art, and I think that's the time that always gives me the idea of what I'm going to do.

We are all having separate therapy, but this has made me realise how important it is to have conversations as a family, which aren't easy to have. When you have someone like Adam, who's very calm, it makes the conversations easier to have. We can articulate how we feel through the art, and that's really showed me how important that can be.

I drew one place, home, Brighton, and the other place, Sheffield, which is where I'm at Uni, and then a line in the middle, with lots of different colours, one showing how I'm feeling torn between the two places, and two showing the emotions that I feel (page 84). It was really nice to do that piece of art, and then afterwards be given the space and the time to talk to my family about it and explain how I'm feeling. And then getting that reassurance from mum in particular, saying that what I'm doing is the right thing for me at the moment. That was really important to me.

I think I gained a lot from art therapy.

Steve

I've never considered myself to be an artist, I have a long standing interest in photography, but I've never attempted to create any art since leaving school. And for this reason, I felt somewhat apprehensive about the prospect of taking part in art therapy.

Adam is very thoughtful, very considerate, and very gentle in his manner. And the sessions are very inclusive. Everybody is made to feel comfortable. And he helped us, myself included, to talk about our feelings and concerns for the pieces we created. I tend to be a fairly positive person, but this has been a challenge given Sam's diagnosis.

We share concerns with each other. However, issues sometimes emerge in art therapy sessions, which we've not previously discussed.

But I always feel very positive and uplifted after one of our sessions with Adam.

I believe that participation in these sessions helped strengthen the links between us and brings us closer together as a family.

On the following pages is a collection of images made by Sam, Steve, Evie and Elise created during our art therapy sessions together, which, they would like to share.

Sam
The Ground of Being

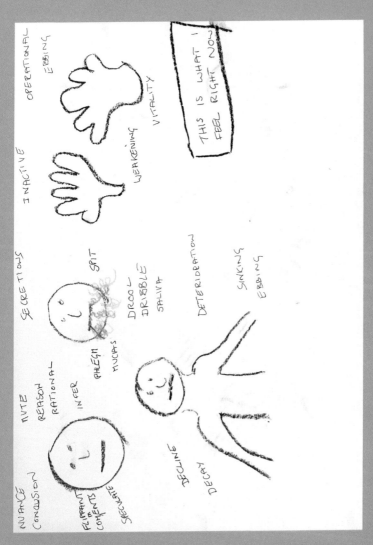

Sam
This Is What I Feel
Right Now

Sam
Rollercoaster

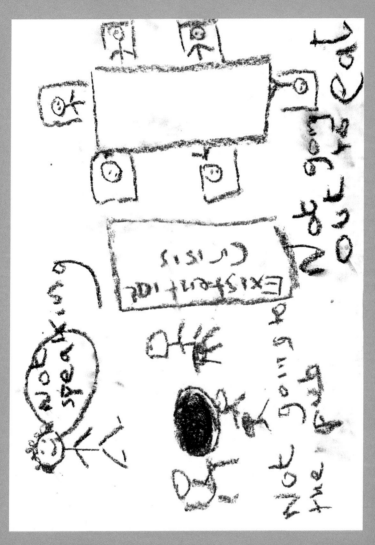

Sam
Existential Crisis

Sam
Where I Am…
Sometimes

Sam
What I Miss

Sam and Steve
Mixed Emotions

Steve
Promenading
with Sam

Evie
Standing Tall

Evie
Emotions

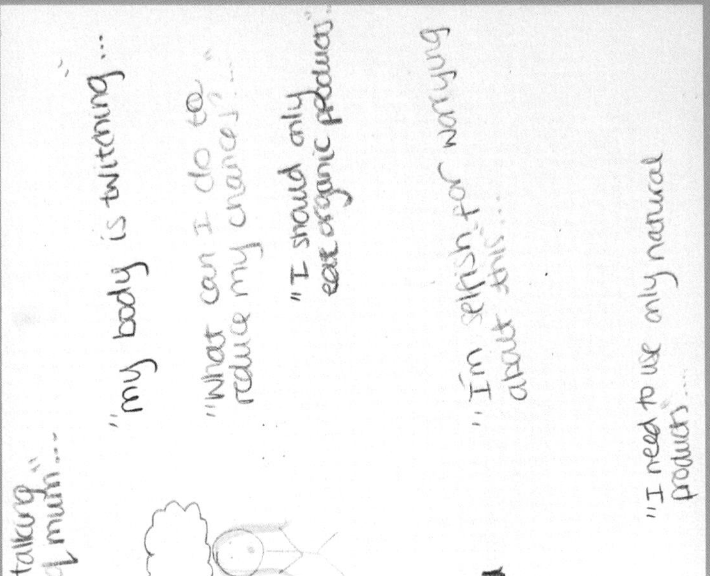

"I'm being insensitive talking about this infront of mum"...

"I just need to stop worrying"...

"do my fingers feel weak"...

"my body is twitching"...

"what can I do to reduce my chance?"...

"I should only eat organic products"...

"can I pronounce certain phrases?"...

"what supplements should I take?"...

"does my grip feel weak"...

"I'm selfish for worrying about this"...

"I need to use only natural products"...

Evie
Familial Fears of
MND

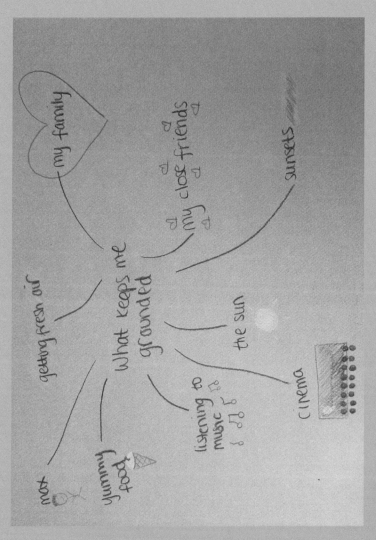

Evie
What Keeps Me
Grounded

joyfully
serious
passionate
listener
socialist
excuberant

loving
kind

morals
caring
fun
outspoken
political
beautiful
unpredictable

cheeky

Evie
The Embodiment
of Mum

Evie and Elise
Together

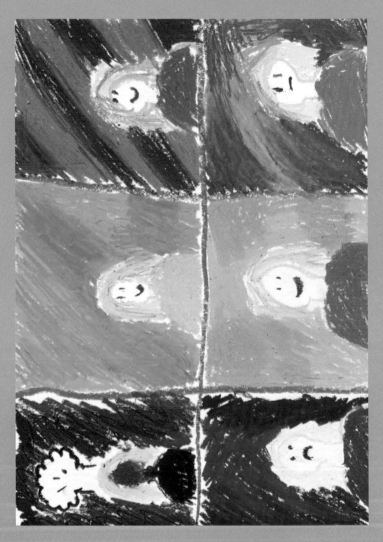

Elise
So Many Emotions

Elise
Broken Yet Full

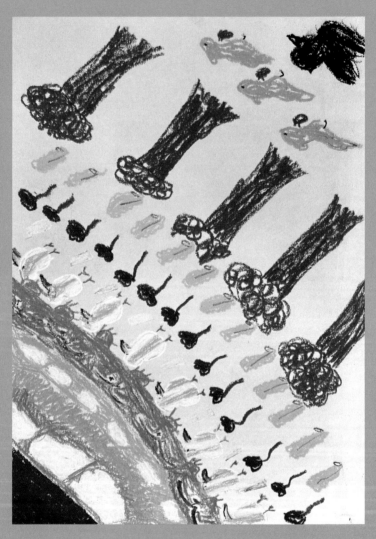

Elise
Brighton Skies

Elise
The Essence
of Mum

Elise
Home | University

Elise
Doing Art Together

Family

Evie   Sam

Elise   Steve

About the MND Association

First established in 1979, the MND Association is the biggest charitable funder of MND research in the UK.

The Association plays a leading role in the global fight against MND, funding groundbreaking research into the disease while facilitating important collaboration between researchers.

While the search for potential new treatments continues, the Association is dedicated to improving access to care, providing support and campaigning on behalf of people affected by MND across England, Wales and Northern Ireland.

The Association funds roles which provide the co-ordination and delivery of care at 22 MND care centres and networks, while its 87 volunteer-led branches and groups provide local support to people with MND, their families and carers. Elsewhere, the Association supports hundreds of health and social care professionals, helping them to learn more about MND through the provision of specialist events and information.

None of this work would be possible without the tremendous support received from its volunteers and from its supporters, who generously donate and fundraise on the Association's behalf.

To learn more about the MND Association, or to make a donation, visit www.mndassociation.org

Registered Charity number: 294354